Everything I Learned

in Life

D1594246

I Learned in

Long Term Care

By

Lori Porter, Co-Founder & CEO

National Association of

Geriatric Nursing Assistants

About the Author

Lori Porter's story of growing up in long term care is a refreshing yet pointed look at life and work in nursing homes. Her 20 plus year career in the nursing home world has taken many twists and turns but, as expressed in this book, has indeed been a journey worth taking. "Everything she learned in life she learned in long term care" is true, and she enthusiastically shares her knowledge with the readers.

Never before has anyone been so honest in their ups, downs, failures, and successes in the world of caring. This book is insightful, thought provoking, and humorous. It describes Lori's journey to becoming a nursing home administrator and tells how she became overpowered by the desire to bring life and laughter to those who needed it most.

In 1995, she realized that caring for the nation's frail, elderly, and disabled meant caring for those who provide the care – the nursing assistants. No one deserves more honor and glory than those who bear the title CNA. Their sacrifices could no longer go unnoticed, so she co-founded the first professional association of nursing assistants known as the National Association of Geriatric Nursing Assistants (NAGNA) with over 22,000 members nationwide and growing rapidly. She is determined to bring recognition to the women and men who serve our elderly, believing it is not only deserved but the best possible way to ensure quality care and quality life to nursing home residents and others who are dependent on nursing assistants for their personal needs.

Lori is a nationally known and requested motivational speaker and consultant. She currently serves as the Chief Operating Officer for NAGNA where she continues to be committed to CNA recognition and personal and professional development.

Contents

FOREWORD

As a registered nurse and licensed nursing home administrator with more than 20 years of service in the long term care profession, I have long known that certified nursing assistants (CNAs) are the secrets of success in our nation's nursing facilities. Overworked and under paid, all the while performing some of the most intimate and, at times, unglamorous, although necessary, functions, CNAs tirelessly strive to make easier what are sometimes the most uncomfortable and lonely days of many residents' long lives.

Throughout my career, I have watched these dedicated workers bathe, feed, wash, turn, and comfort our most frail, elderly or disabled citizens. I have observed these heroes go beyond their job descriptions as they forge lasting friendships with the residents for whom they care. Their commitment to their work and the compassion in their hearts inspires me today.

Thanks to Lori Porter's *Everything I Learned in Life I Learned in Long Term Care*, and her other work on behalf of CNAs, they are finally getting the recognition they deserve. It is impossible to read Porter's professional life story without being struck by the effect she has had on the lives of countless others – both residents of and caregivers in long term care facilities. In recounting her experiences, Porter invites her readers on a journey of self-discovery that is at times painful, often funny, and always moving. And it is this evolution – this roller coaster ride – that no doubt makes a career in nurse assisting so challenging. Luckily, hundreds of thousands of CNAs accept these challenges every day.

It is my hope that, like Porter, other CNAs feel that they have achieved personal growth through their work. If there were one thing I'd like readers to take away from this book, it is that a life of service to the elderly and disabled is a life well lived. *Everything I Learned in Life I Learned in Long Term Care* shows that success is attainable once you allow yourself to think successfully. Of course, the ultimate example of this in the author's own life is the creation of the National Association of Geriatric Nursing Assistants (NAGNA). The brainchild of Porter and co-founder Lisa Cantrell, NAGNA now represents more than 30,000 CNAs representing more than 500 nursing homes in 29 states and the District of Columbia.

It is through NAGNA that Porter has been able to achieve success on one of her ultimate goals: creating an environment where CNAs are each other's greatest advocates. This insightful book details a phenomenon Porter witnessed first-hand, where CNAs too often degraded one another and their work. As the author notes in one of the most important of several "life lessons" that are sprinkled throughout the text, "The attitude of CNAs toward their peers has more influence than does administration. Change the attitude of the CNAs from negative to positive and it will change the whole facility and eventually all of long term care."

Porter's commitment to CNAs and the populations they serve is a lesson in and of itself. *Everything I Learned in Life I Learned in Long Term Care* is a guide to selfless giving and enduring optimism, two attributes a CNA should not be without.

Mary K. Ousley

Mary K. Ousley

Mary K. Ousley is the Executive Vice President, SunBridge Healthcare Corporation. SunBridge Healthcare operates more than 250 skilled nursing, long-term care facilities and assisted living residences throughout the United States.

Ms. Ousley has held multiple leadership positions in dynamic healthcare corporations, which have provided her with an extensive background in, and in-depth knowledge of all facets of the long-term-care profession. In addition to Ms. Ousley's professional leadership, she is an active member of the long-term care profession.

She is the current Chairman of the American Health Care Association, the largest trade organization representing long-term care. Mary is the first nurse to be Chairman of AHCA and the first woman to hold the seat in 50 years. Since 1988, she has acted as an Advisory Provider Representative to the Centers for Medicare and Medicaid. She is currently serving on the CMS & Quality Improvement Organization's Nursing Facility Technical Expert Panel on the development and implementation of a quality improvement model for long-term care.

She serves on the Health and Human Services and Robert Wood Johnson Foundation National Steering Committee focusing on the future of the paraprofessional long-term care workforce.

Ms. Ousley received her degree from Eastern Kentucky University and in 1990 was recognized by the University College of Nursing as the outstanding alumna, in recognition of a registered nurse who has made significant contributions to the field of nursing on a local, state, and national level.

Dedication

To Lisa who helped me realize a dream in more ways than one. To my mom who made all things possible at a great sacrifice to herself. To Matt and Laci who provided me with joy throughout the process. To the many residents I cared for and learned many valuable lessons from. And most importantly, to the great CNA humanitarians I have been privileged to meet along the way.

Chapter One

A Kid Looks at Life in a Nursing Home

I was born in Baxter Springs, Kansas, in the early sixties. I remember going with my mother to visit an elderly friend of hers who was living in a nursing home and wondering what was wrong with her and the other residents that would cause them to have to live in a place like this. It didn't occur to me that old age was a condition.

Mrs. Brown was mother's friend, and boy, was she ancient. I sat by the bed while they visited. (There wasn't much for a kid of four years old to do in a nursing home.) It wasn't long before I discovered that old people have flabby arms. Mrs.

Brown had incredibly soft skin, and I wanted to touch it badly but was convinced if I was to be so bold, it would embarrass my mother, and in turn, she would slap me out of my chair. My desire got the best of me – I had to touch that flabby, soft skin. Finally, I could not resist any longer, and my right hand went for it. Once my mom discovered it, she nearly died on the spot. "Lori, stop that right now." She apologized to Mrs. Brown, but the old friend said, "Oh, honey, let her have her way. She's not bothering me; it actually feels pretty good." I thought yes, it does to me to.

Well, Mrs. Brown saved me; I didn't get in trouble, and I had a way of occupying my time while on the visits. It also brought smiles to Mrs.

Brown's face so how could it be bad. Who knew this was a glimpse of things to come.

I don't remember when Mrs. Brown died, but I do know she gave us an antique coffee table that has been in my mother's living room everyday since. It is a beautiful piece of furniture and a constant reminder of Mrs. Brown's arms.

The next time I visited a nursing home was to see my Grandma. My parents had divorced when I was seven, and my mom, sister, and I had moved to southwest Missouri. My dad's mother was, as I remember, a very good grandma – the cookie-baking kind with tender words. She had been placed in a nursing home, and on one of my visits with Dad, he took me to see her. I was in the seventh grade. (I think it was the same nursing home Mrs. Brown had lived in.) I remembered thinking how could dad or his brothers and sisters put Grandma in a place like this? Why can't they take care of her at home? It wasn't long after that that Grandma died.

The nursing home she lived in is still open today. A few updates in furnishings but essentially life is still the same today as it was then. Many people have come and gone from there – Mrs. Brown, Grandma, and countless others. I am just thankful I got to know a few. Who knew I would be destined for a nursing home career. Certainly not me. Liking old people and taking care of them are two very different things.

Life Lesson # 1
The young and the old have a lot to offer one another, among these are the value of a touch and a smile. I learned at a very early age that it was a pleasant experience to touch an old person and that it was a means of communication.

Chapter Two

A Chance of a Lifetime – A Dietary Aide at 17

I had a very eventful childhood and would not have changed a thing. We were poor in money but rich in fun and spirit. I was not a particularly good student, but I was a fairly good basketball player and had fought hard to see a girl's program started in the school system. (It wasn't until eighth grade that it finally happened.) I had made the boy's team in sixth grade, but the school board ruled I couldn't play. A series of things occurred during my high school years that led me to quit the sport I loved. No one was more shocked than I the day I said enough is enough and made the long walk off the court and through the exit doors. Soon after, I quit school. I announced to my mother, "Yesterday was my last day of school." She said, "Did you graduate early?" I said, "No Mom, I quit."

I had gotten addicted to soap operas in the summer between my sophomore and junior year. I had not told anyone of my dream, but what I really wanted to do was move to New York City and get a job as a soap opera actress. It hadn't occurred to me that I'm not actress material in terms of body and beauty. Well, before I could say what my plans were, Mother had another plan. She said, "Well, honey, if you are not going to go to school you are going to go to work." Uh, oh. Work? I can't go to work. First off, there is nowhere to work. In this small town, you had three choices – the dairy cone, the chicken plant, and the nursing home. Not much to choose from but my first choice was the dairy cone. You see, the thought of working at the chicken plant or even the nursing home made me physically ill. I had a very weak stomach, and the old folks scared me with their whiskers, yellow fingernails, and hollering out. The thought of plucking, cutting, and deboning chicken made me almost as ill. So I said dairy cone, here I come.

Mother had other plans. She was the dietary manager of our local nursing home and needed a dishwasher. She had me earmarked for the position. Thankfully, I remembered her saying once that the facility had a policy that prohibited supervisors from hiring relatives in their departments. I quickly reminded Mother of the policy. She fired back, "Lucky for you I got special permission!"

Let me assure you, when you are 17 years old and get a job working in a nursing home you do not call up your best friends and say, "Guess what? I just got the opportunity of a lifetime. I have been hired on down at the nursing home!" It is more popular to work at the chicken plant than taking care of old people. First off, I had the weakest stomach of anyone I had ever met. How was I going to be able to work around the old people? They all seemed to be creepy. I mean they had yellow, thick fingernails, talked to themselves, and were often drooling or had food on their clothes. The smell was not appealing either. I know what you are thinking – our facility doesn't have an odor problem. Right! Oh, I know some are much better than others but to an outsider, all nursing homes have odors. Oh well, my destiny was set, and I had no choice.

I begrudgingly began my fancy job as a dishwasher at the 100-bed, skilled nursing home. I stayed in the kitchen never venturing out. I lived in fear that a resident would wander in needing help to the toilet or having already had an accident. Occasionally it happened, and I always grabbed the intercom and paged the nurse to dietary STAT! My stomach was so weak that watching the garbage swirling around in the disposal made me feel ill.

Mother was a good dietary manager, always winning awards for outstanding food and for staying under her budgeted food cost. I soon graduated to the relief cook position. It was a chance to be creative, or so I thought. I inherited a knack for home cooking and was eager to give the residents a taste of some of my specialties which at the time was fried chicken, fried potatoes, and greens. Sounds pretty good, doesn't it? I had both the residents and staff hanging around the kitchen begging for even a dripping from the pan. I would oblige when possible. My competitive spirit took over, and I was determined to be the best cook long term care had ever seen. I may have been, but I had a little run in with the menu.

Low salt was not in my vocabulary. The word diabetic meant nothing to me when a person had made it to 70; damn it, let them eat pie was my philosophy. I cooked the way the residents and staff wanted to eat, not the way the conservative medicine and unrealistic regulations dictated they eat. Needless to say, I was popular with the people I was hired to serve but in complete violation with the establishment. I tried to tone it down a bit, but making people happy was more important to me than following the rules. I would get rid of the bacon grease before the surveyors made it back to the kitchen. Thank goodness today things are a bit less restrictive. I am sure it makes the cooks' professional life a lot more rewarding.

Life Lesson # 2
**If you can't do what you want to do,
be the best at what you have to do.**

Chapter Three

Use Caution When Accepting Extra Hours

Early on, while I was still washing dishes, I had an experience that would set the stage for the remainder of my career. After a few weeks of keeping myself locked away in the kitchen pretending I was working at a McDonalds or Hardees, I finally grew tired of the drink selection we had in the kitchen which consisted of the usual fruit juices – cranberry, orange, apple, and of course, prune. I have to say this – those were the most regular days of my life, if you get my meaning. Anyway, I ventured out to the breakroom to purchase a soda. While there, I observed three nursing assistants having a conversation. They did not look particularly happy so I eavesdropped a bit and heard them talking about being low man on the totem pole, peons, and one even said, "Butt wipers, that's what we are." I couldn't believe it. Then as I started to walk out the door, one of them reached up, nudged me in the shoulder and said in a gruff voice, "When you gonna come work the floor with us, get yourself a real job?" I was in such shock all I could do was say to her, "I will never do what you do." After all, they were not doing a very good sales pitch on the job, and plus, I had the weakest stomach in the world, not to mention one of my greatest fears was being near a resident when they peed, pooped, or threw up. It seemed logical to say

NEVER! Doesn't it take a special person to be a CNA? Of course. Well, I was the first to admit there wasn't anything special about me.

Have you ever said never and almost immediately found yourself doing what you said you would never do? By now, I had turned 18, and it appeared to Mother that I was never going to leave home so she was going to have to. She announced she was moving to Atlanta, Georgia. My question was, "How am I going to survive alone on what I make in dietary?" She suggested I get a second job.

Our administrator soon offered to find me some additional hours at the facility. I thought this was a nice jester on her part. I saw she had posted a notice near the time clock looking for someone to help out taking care of the grounds, assisting the maintenance man with mowing, watering, and flower maintenance. I thought this was what she had in mind being I was an athletic, strong young woman. I quickly said, "Oh, extra hours would be great." A few minutes passed and the intercom rang back in the kitchen. It was the administrator saying, "I found you some hours. We have a full-time 3:00 to 11:00 nursing aide position open, and we're holding it for you!" I said, "Let it go – you got the wrong girl for this one."

The bad thing was Mother was still there with 28 days left to work out her notice. She knew exactly what was going on, and she said, "You look here. You are not going to turn this down. It's a great offer. Many of those hours will be overtime so you say yes, because you are going to take those hours, work them, and do a good job. You are not going to ruin my reputation here young lady. You are going to take those hours, and YOU WILL NOT QUIT!" I thought, you want to bet, "I can't be a CNA". I can barely work in dietary. With 28 days left and counting, I knew it would be impossible to get out of being a CNA for at least that long. Somehow, someway, I had to make it through CNA orientation and actually be one. I could not imagine how this was going to happen. I did not have the character, the desire, the passion, not even the compassion. Nowhere did I have anything to draw from to get the strength to make myself do this.

I found the strength, but at the time, I didn't know it was coming from following the lead of a parent. You would have to know Mother to know where she got her strength. I know for most of my mother's life she did what she had to do, rarely getting to do what she wanted to do. For the first time, she was in a place where she could experience life and have some fun. She had graduated college at 50 and was ready to have some experiences on her own. No doubt she had earned that right given all her sacrifices for her children, especially me.

Mother had survived cancer when the doctors said she wouldn't. She had crushed her ankle, and doctors said she would likely never walk well again, if at all. She proved them wrong. When I was a baby, she was trying to get the old water pump in the barn to work in the dead of winter when one of her fingers got caught in the belt and was nearly cut off leaving only a sliver of skin attached while the finger hung down. The doctor prepared to clip that sliver of skin when she said, "What are you doing?" He said, "Removing your finger." "No," she said, "You sew it back on." He said, "Ruby, I can't sew it on – it won't grow; it will die. There is no way to reconnect all those tiny nerves and such." She said, "You sew it on, and I will make it grow." Well folks, that was 1962, and she still has her finger. There is a tiny line of motor oil under the skin which serves as a reminder of her will and determination. Telling Mother you couldn't was never an option. If she could do the impossible, so could you. And I did!

Life Lesson # 3
It sometimes seems that by the time you say the words "I will NEVER do that," fate has made it such that with your next breath you are having to figure out a way to do that exact thing. Destiny rarely leads you in the direction you thought you were going – usually you are led into a certain path for a reason. Make it count!

Chapter Four

You Want Me to Do What?

Knowing I was anxious about the new position, the administrator assured me I would be fine because she was going to put me with their best nursing assistant who had been there seven years and had never missed a day. She could get more people up, make more beds, and feed more people – I mean whatever was called for she could do it better and faster than anyone else. The residents loved her, and she loved the residents. By all accounts, she was indeed the best nursing assistant. They called her the "mentor." I was so relieved to know they were handling me with kid gloves, really looking out for me, or so I thought. You know, if this lady is everything she's cracked up to be I might be able to get through the next 27 evenings without ever having to do peri care.

Well, my first evening started off with a bang. I heard the CNAs had taken bets on how long I would last, and I'm sure my fellow dietary comrades were involved as well. Heck, I would have bet against me. First off, I had no intentions of lasting. My only salvation was privately planning my escape on the 28th day. As soon as the U-haul and Mother's car were out of sight, I was going to make that my last day as a CNA! I had the exit door picked where I could slip out undetected. I planned to park close to the door thinking I could be gone at least 30 minutes before anyone realized. I had no intentions of coming back to pick up a paycheck or anything. I was going to blow the dietary and CNA jobs off immediately. Even though I liked cooking, my thinking at the time was if I quit the CNA job without notice, they will never let me cook, so it was all or nothing. In my mind, it was well worth it just to get out of my personal hell.

I worked days in dietary so I did not really know this "mentor" woman they were putting me with for orientation. As I said, I had high expectations. If she was all she was set up to be, I was going to be protected and eased into the CNA experience. I had been given the usual set of paperwork to complete before starting my new post.

While completing the paperwork, I was approached by my mentor for the first time. She was a tough, old broad, always pulling up her scrubs by the waist band while spouting some tall tail about how good she was. She wasn't being egotistical, but you know how some CNAs like to brag. I'd hear things like, "No one else can give Mr. Hodges a bath, but by golly, I took him in there and did it. I mean, don't get me wrong – he spit on me twice, pulled a handful of my hair out, and kicked me in the shin, but I got him." It was like she was telling old war stories to impress me. All the while, I am thinking what a fool. Who wants to brag about getting abused?

She looked down and saw I was reading the job description as part of my paperwork requirement. She started chuckling and said in her tough voice, "Job description; honey, let me tell you about your job description! You're gonna wipe some butts, your gonna wipe some more butts, and when you are all through with that your gonna wipe a whole lot more butts – now that's the job description. Sign it at the bottom, and let's get busy." I knew right then I was done for. There would be no easy ride with this lady.

We took off down the hall, and I watched from afar – just as far back as I could get. She was actually pretty good at allowing me to assist by getting clothes out of the closet and handing her things. We were getting residents up for the evening meal, and other than a few things, like seeing a catheter for the first time, it was not too bad. If she was cleaning someone up, I conveniently was rummaging through the closet or drawers.

I had made it unscathed up to 9:30 that evening. I was almost home free when the mentor says to me, "The charge nurse just told me Mr. Smith in 401 has just had a BM accident." She said, "Sugar, this is where we see what you're made of." Excuse me? She said, "You need to go on down there and take care of him. You have been watching me all evening, and now it's time you do one on your own." I'm thinking, "ON MY OWN, is she crazy? What do I do, how can I do it?" Well, refusing was not an option. I was too intimidated to speak up, so I told myself, you can do this – somehow, someway you can do this.

I decided to do the job I would need tools. I went to the clean utility room in search of aerosol spray; that was a must. While in there, I found two of those paper masks with the strings. I tied both of them on. You know, in 1980 you couldn't find gloves in nursing homes. Now they hang on every wall, but back then real nurse aides didn't wear gloves! Facilities didn't buy gloves. It was long before universal precautions came into play, and anything we got on our fingers, we could just wash off. I don't know why they were there, but lucky for me, underneath the sink, was a pair of those orange dishwashing gloves. I put them on, and away I went with the aerosol spray under my arm, the paper masks tied around my nose and mouth, and the dishwashing gloves nearly up to my elbows.

I know I was a sight, and I knew they would laugh, but my motto was to do whatever it takes to get this done because soon it will be over. I started spraying long before I got to Mr. Smith's door. I was inhaling as much of the spray into my lungs as I could get. I know I was in his room at least 30 minutes, maybe longer. When you are 18 years old and see the first ever 80-year-old, naked man, it takes a few minutes to overcome it. Now, I know in this business CNAs and nurses will often say if you can take care of a baby, you can take care of an old person. Well, I am here to tell you this is not true! Stop telling this lie. I have taken care of both, and there is quite a big difference!

I finally accomplished the goal and exited the room. I know I had turned green and was positive I was going to vomit. I looked up the hall and saw the nursing assistants and two charge nurses standing there looking down at me with puzzled looks on their faces. I wasn't sure why they were looking; I guess to see if I would come out screaming, puking, or crying. I walked right past them headed for the breakroom where I could get a cold cloth and a 7UP. I sat next to the trash can knowing any second I was going to hurl. In walks the "mentor." She pats me on the back and says in her deep voice, "Sugar, you're gonna have to toughen up. I've been doing this so long I can wipe a butt with one hand and eat a sandwich with the other one!" I didn't know that was the goal! And if it was, I was never going to achieve it.

That night I drove home praying to die. I thought, there is no way out of this – 26 nights are too much – I can't take it, and I certainly won't make it. I couldn't quit because of Mother so death seemed like the only way out. Now you know you are in the wrong profession when death seems more desirable then the job. I thought just let a Mack truck hit me or something. Well, that didn't happen. I woke up the next morning in good condition. Off to work I went to cook breakfast and lunch for the residents. It wasn't as much fun because all I could think about was 3:00 coming and how awful it was going to be.

Life Lesson # 4
The only way to overcome fear
is to make yourself do what seems
to be the impossible.
Nothing is ever as bad as it seems once it has
been accomplished.

Chapter Five

Round Two With the Mentor

Day two of orientation, and I can't believe I am back – 25 shifts and counting before escape. We started our shift by loading linen carts, getting residents up for showers, and of course, getting them up for the evening meal. We went into one gentleman's room which I will never forget. The mentor handed me some tiny little stockings and said for me to put them on him. I was shocked because this guy must have weighed at least 300 pounds, and I was sure she was mistaken or else was setting me up for a big joke. (I was still intimidated and afraid to buck the system so I played along.) She was busy getting clothes out of the closet as I began to put the first stocking on him. It was a chore! I was pulling and twisting and working up quite a sweat when I finally got the first one up over his knee. I immediately pulled it off, and she jumped right in saying to me, "What are you doing? It took you ten minutes to put it on." I said, "I know but the dang thing isn't any good; it has a hole in the toe!" She yelled back, "They're Ted hose!" I thought I had it figured out. I said, "This isn't Ted." My logic was we got the wrong guy – these socks belonged to a little fella named Ted that I hadn't met yet. "No," she said. "That's what they're called." Now how is a two-day, uncertified nursing assistant supposed to know what Ted hose are?

Later that evening I heard them laughing around the nurse's station saying, "Can you believe she didn't know what Ted hose were?" They never knew I heard, but I hated them for it. On top of hating the job, I hated my coworkers and immediate supervisors. The only people I liked were the administrator and director of nursing, but like all new people, I was turned over to the masses for training.

Now they might have called my orientator a mentor, but I had another name for her! Now, now, now, I know what you are thinking, but what I called her (to myself that is) was "Tormentor."

Right now would be a good time for you, the reader, to ask yourself, are you a mentor or a tormentor?

My biggest mistake was thinking things couldn't possibly get worse. I think it was maybe the third evening when one of our residents wasn't doing very well. The day before she was alert, oriented, and flirting with the doctor; the next, she was out of her head, screaming obscenities, and hollering the name Maxine! In report, we learned she had gone into congestive heart failure and probably would not live to the end of our shift. I remember thinking how can anyone change so quickly. We checked on her frequently making sure she was as comfortable as possible, but about 10:00 she passed away. I was sad for her because I had gotten to know her. She was active in resident council and had visited me in the kitchen many times to compliment my food. Quickly, my sadness turned to shock when the mentor said, "Sugar, you're gonna have to learn this sooner or later – might as well be now. "Learn what?" I asked. "Post mortem care." "What's that?" "You'll see," she said. "Follow me."

In the room, she began to say, "You need to brush her hair." "Excuse me?" "Yes, brush her hair, then clean her dentures and put them in her mouth." I said, "Look, I know you hurried me through the job description, but I don't remember reading anything about this. Isn't this what a funeral home is for?" She said, "The family is on their way in, and she needs to be cleaned up before they arrive. We want them to see her at peace like they remember her." I was scared to death. It was dark; the only light on was the over-bed light. When we began to change her gown, each time the mentor would roll her my way, her eyes popped open at me. Oh, I was so freaked out! Then, out of nowhere, the mentor says, "You wait here. I have to go to the linen room for more sheets." Inside my head I am screaming "oh, dear God, don't leave me here alone!"

I made it through orientation only because I had no choice. I was enrolled in CNA class and working two jobs under one roof. The nursing home was my home.   All this and still nothing

special about me.

Life Lesson # 5
At the time (though not realizing it), I was learning how caring and devoted a CNA must be to care for the dead as well as the living. To tackle an unpleasant job is not a piece of cake – it takes courage and a special person. CNAs are special people.

Chapter Six

Never Say Never
(dedicated to Ms. Gladys Punton)

I'm on my own and in charge of providing care under the direction of LPN and RN charge nurses. Still secretly planning my escape, I was even more determined to get out of there the first chance I had. But one day my plans changed. I went around the corner to get something from the linen closet when I noticed a call light going off nearby. You know how every nursing home has at least one resident that when they put on their light everyone scatters? I mean, you will do anything not to get caught by that light, even bargaining with coworkers. (If you will answer that light, I will make all your beds.) Well, I did not have sense enough to run so I decided to answer the light. I knew the resident by reputation only. She was a real pain – very demanding and treated nursing assistants like her servants. She had a million little requirements for everything she did. I heard someone say that it takes 45 minutes every time she wants the bed pan. I am not sure why I answered that light. It was not like me to go out of my way to assist the nursing assistants because they had treated me so rotten. I wasn't getting attached to the residents because well, I was leaving. Whatever it was that took me to that room is why I am still in long term care today.

Ms. Punton was a beautiful old woman. I mean more than beautiful – she was stunning, that is from the neck up. She always demanded we keep the sheet pulled up so people could only see her from the neck up because her body was so mangled with arthritis. She wanted makeup applied each morning so passersby could only see her beauty and not her deformities. She did seem vain but people are not always as they seem – a lesson I was about to learn the hard way.

"Ms. Punton, how can I help you?" I asked. She said, "I need to use the restroom." "Would you like the bed pan?" "No," she replied. "I think I want to go into the toilet." OK, now I'm in for it. I have my own residents to care for; this is not my hall, and I do not have time to mess with this lady. If it takes 45 minutes for the bedpan, it's going to take an hour or more for the toilet. I reluctantly, and without a lot of patience, began the arduous task of getting her decrepit, old body out of bed and to the bathroom. Finally, we are there. I get her on the toilet. She is so pitiful. I mean, she has a beautiful face and classy hair but a worn-out, doubled-over body which causes her enormous pain.

She lets me know right away that she needs a warm wash cloth, a cold one, a cool one, a hot one, and a dry one. I bet there were 15 wash clothes required for this activity. Once prepared, she starts requesting them one by one. Each time she asks for one, I do a big sigh and hand it to her. All the while I am sighing and shifting from hip to hip, I am thinking to myself, man, if I were she and in this shape, I would make people wait on me hand and foot. I also thought wouldn't it be nice to be so beautiful at her age. After a few minutes of communicating to her through my body language and frequent sighs, she looks up at me in the most pitiful way and says, "Honey, if you do not have more patience than that for the little old people, maybe you have picked the wrong line of work." Now, the amazing thing is that I did not say, "Lady, you're not telling me anything I do not already know. I have been looking for a way out of here for the past three weeks." Instead, something else happened. Number one, I was completely ashamed. I don't believe I have ever been more ashamed. Here I was thinking how beautiful she was and what I would do if I were she, but on the other hand I was disrespecting her with my actions.

Having a revelation at 18 years old is probably not very common, but it happened to me. At that minute, I knew there was nowhere else a high school dropout could go and have that much power and influence. Each of us has an amazing power, and the only control we have over it is how we use it. That day, I had used my power in the most despicable way. I had disrespected Ms. Punton at her most vulnerable moment. I suspect I could not have disrespected her more if I had slapped her in the face. Chances are she would have preferred that over what I did. You see, we have the power to make an old person feel special, beautiful, worthwhile, needed, wanted, respected, revered, admired, and productive, but we also have the power to strip them of their every dignity. That power should come with a warning, and we should all be reminded of it everyday. None of us fully appreciate or comprehend the power of our own influence.

I never apologized to Ms. Punton. I never had to. I repaid her by requesting her hall from then on. Of course, no one objected; they were glad to give up that assignment. Oh, and by the way, I also realized that in those three weeks I was a nursing assistant and not doing too bad of a job at it until that point. If I would put as much energy into finding out a way to stay as I had in finding a way to quit, I could probably do OK. I also decided if I were going to be a good nursing assistant, I was going to have to change the way I looked, the way I walked, talked, acted, and the way I thought.

Life Lesson # 6
Actions speak louder than words.
The only way to gain respect is
to earn it by conduct.

Chapter Seven

Look at Her – She Thinks She's a Doctor

First order of business was the wardrobe. I borrowed some money from my brother to go buy a uniform. To this point, I had worn only white jeans, tennis shoes, and some kind of white shirt. Before selecting a uniform, I decided to do a bit of research. Since I had made this commitment to be a good nursing assistant, I wanted to be sure and get all the respect and recognition I could, and I wanted to be noticed.

I watched to see who got the respect, who was treated the best, and what made it so. One common theme was dress – those who dressed the best were treated better. Since our appearance casts the first impression, it is important to look your best. I noticed the nurses seemed to dress professionally and were treated with a fair measure of respect. So I thought OK, I will dress like a nurse. I went to the uniform shop and picked out a uniform and lab coat. (Most charge nurses wore lab coats, so I assumed it was an essential part of the professional package.) I had my items on the counter. The clerk was ringing them up when I noticed on display a bright red and silver stethoscope, and I knew I had to have it. I had no idea what it cost, but it had to be mine. I wasn't thinking about blood pressures; I was thinking about jewelry. Man, this would really set this outfit off! It was under 10 bucks so I bought it. I might have been all right if I would have stopped there, but no, I had to get the pocket protector with the scissors and tape. (You never know when you're going to be called on to assist the nurse with a procedure, and I wanted to be prepared.)

I will never forget arriving to work that evening. I didn't even make it to the time clock when I heard one of the other CNAs say, "Look at her, she thinks she's a doctor." I just walked on. It seemed to me that nursing assistants are going to make fun of you no matter what – whether you don't know what Ted hose are on day two or if on day 20 you have committed yourself to be the best nursing assistant you can be and take pride in how you look. Oh well, if I am going to be made fun of better to have it happen because I am trying to do my best. I must say it worked. I immediately moved up on the list of nursing assistants my charge nurses looked for when they needed to have a question answered or to get some important feedback on a situation or a resident's condition. I felt valued.

My uniform and lab coat were starched so heavily they could stand up in the corner. I had some coworkers whose uniforms would also stand up in the corner, but it had nothing to do with starch, if you get my drift. They were also usually the ones who made fun of people like me for trying. I have never fully understood, nor will I ever understand, why CNAs sabotage their own working conditions by making fun of new people and taking the risk of running them off. The very thing they complain about most is not having enough help. They can't seem to draw the connection of treating new people with respect and offering mentoring and understanding in hopes of developing a professional.

Life Lesson # 7
To get respect from my superiors,
I learned I had to show respect
for myself and my profession.

Chapter Eight

Losing Good People as a Result of Good People

Over the years, one thing has remained true. The number one reason new nursing assistants quit is not because of the work, not because of the residents, not because of how supervisors treat them, but rather how they are treated by the CNAs. The nursing assistant shortage could all but come to a screeching halt if experienced CNAs would see themselves as mentors to new nursing assistants and act accordingly. I believe it is unintentional and a result of CNAs not understanding the power of their own influence.

It became overwhelming clear to me a few years after starting NAGNA. Using our CNA members, we made a commercial at one of our member facilities. The purpose of the commercial was to recruit citizens in our community to seek a career in long term care and apply for admission in a nursing assistant certification school NAGNA was piloting. The commercial was a huge hit in that it drew a large number of people to the school. As a matter of fact, within the first 48 hours of airing on the local network, 27 people had come in to complete the application for acceptance. WOW, what a success!

I was so proud of the work our members had done with the commercial that I took a copy to the facility to show the CNAs. Their first words following the showing were "If it were only that glamorous." Now we did not depict the position as anything other than what it was. We showed CNAs assisting residents with meals, dressing, shaving, walking, range of motion, and vital signs. We used upbeat music and graphics. It depicted the job as professional and important which, by the way, it is. So, no lies were told, but yet the CNAs involved saw the job as anything but glamorous.

I believe we could be graced with a million new nursing assistants entering the field today and within three weeks, we would be short-handed. Despite management's every effort (and ever-wasted advertising dollar), any measure of success can be sabotaged by the CNAs as a result of this phenomenon. The power of one's influence is rarely ever thought about or even recognized.

During a workshop I was presenting several years ago in a member facility with approximately 30 CNAs present, I was talking about this very issue. One CNA agreed with me out loud. She said, "We are guilty of this, and I know because I was treated that way when I started." I remember feeling good that someone had validated my thoughts so publicly. The workshop was being held in the facility dining room and after another 15 minutes had passed, and we were on a new subject, a young woman came in from outside and approached the office reception window. She was clearly awaiting an application when the very CNA who minutes ago had validated my comments on how we treat new people stood up and said, "Quick, somebody get an application; there's fresh meat!" Can you believe it? I was so shocked, I was almost speechless. Relax, I said, some things almost never change. After a moment I jumped on the chance to address the situation. See, even when CNAs agree with the phenomenon, they cannot easily change their actions. This is not an easy cycle to break, but it is not impossible. I have been proud to watch the transformation of our members over the years into protectors of the inexperienced. They truly understand that no new nursing assistant can be any better than the example the members set for them.

One other example which demonstrates this clearly is the situation that followed our first graduating class from our CNA certification school. Our students completed an 80-hour clinical in a nearby member facility. For two weeks they gave all the baths, worked the dining room, and assisted the CNAs with ADLs and whatever else was asked of them. The administrator and nursing director treated them with respect in hopes they would come back as employees once they had received their certification. Historically, we know that a person is more likely to seek employment where they completed their clinicals because they are already somewhat familiar with the residents, routines, and staff.

There were 15 students in the first class. At the end of the program, we always hosted a job fair where all area facilities were invited to come interview the new graduates and to be interviewed by them. All seven area facilities attended in hopes of hiring the graduates. The facility where the clinicals had been conducted arrived bearing gifts in hopes to cinch the deal and hire all 15 graduates. They made offers to each. At the end of the day, all but one selected other facilities than the clinical site. The administrator and nursing director were in shock, as was I. After everyone left, I asked the class why they had not accepted the clinical site as their employer. They said the administrator and director of nursing were great, but every time they went into the breakroom, the CNAs said, "You do not want to go to work for this dump!"

It is amazing the power of influence CNAs yield in this area. One of my main purposes in life is to reverse this phenomenon. That has been my focus and that of our Association. We transform people into the kind who are accommodating and nurturing to the new nursing assistants just as they are to their residents.

Life Lesson # 8
**The attitude of CNAs toward their peers
has more influence than does administration.
Change the attitude of the CNAs from
negative to positive and it will
change the whole facility and eventually all
of long term care.**

Chapter Nine

A Fall From Grace

The phenomenon has a further reach than I thought. Despite my best attempts of clinging to my commitment to be a great nursing assistant, I failed. You see, a CNA spends more time with coworkers than the supervisors. The administrator and nursing director were very good to me and so were the charge nurses for the most part, but unfortunately, I was not around them enough to combat the negativity and influence from the coworkers. Now, don't get me wrong. The coworkers were generally good CNAs committed to the residents, but in the privacy of the breakroom or at a social event, they let their frustration run freely with rhetoric about how undervalued and unappreciated we were, not to mention underpaid. It was also common to blame management for our problems. Soon I began to change my perspective, and before long, I was not only joining in the discussion, I was often the leader.

I finally left the facility in search of greener pastures. The next facility was worse, and I do mean worse. Now I wasn't blessed with supervisors who knew me, so I was automatically categorized by whatever view the supervisors had of CNAs. I no longer felt valued, and after a period, I left to go back to where life had been better.

I still had not given myself the mental enema necessary to return to the CNA I had been earlier in my career. I had been back about six months and already written up once or twice for my bad attitude when I took the liberty one evening to spout off some complaints about the way things were being handled at the facility. After a few minutes, an elderly CNA who worked evening shift with us but did not typically socialize or even talk to us younger CNAs looked at me from the opposite end of the break table and said something like "How long have you worked here now?" I said, "Six months this time, and it has been the longest six months of my life." She said, "Well, I have been here 12 years, and it has been the longest six months of my life too!" Uh, oh! Now that will shut you down immediately. I was stunned, but before I could speak she went on to say, "You're a pretty good nurse aide, but your attitude is going to kill you. We need nurse aides, but we do not need anyone that badly. You see, this place means something to me, and I am not going to sit here and listen to you tear it down." What could I say? What were my options? I thought about telling her off, but I could tell the others in the room had a look like "thank God someone finally said something to her." I quickly thought about reporting her; who did she think she was telling me what to do. Then I thought, who would believe me? I've been written up, and she has never missed a day of work. They would tell me to get over it.

I realized my only choices were to get better or quit. I chose to get better. I learned a valuable lesson that evening. I learned what it takes for someone to stand up for what they believed in. Stella stood up for her profession, her facility, and her residents. The smartest thing I ever did was take heed of the meaning of what had happened and how to use the technique in my own career.

As professional CNAs, we have to learn to take ownership in our careers and to stand up for what we believe in. Too often we are noted as taking the side of those who complain when we are really sick of hearing it, but because we do nothing, we are indirectly encouraging them to continue. If we stand up for what we believe in, we have power and other people will follow our lead. We can make a great difference if all CNAs will take heed and learn this technique.

Years later in my administrator career, Stella and I met again. (Stay tuned; you'll read about our reunion in another chapter.) I have had an amazing career in long term care, and I owe most of it to Stella who spoke up to make her position known and stood behind it. It took courage to do that. It takes risking not being the most popular, but the payoff is amazing. One of the most important things it taught me was to have courage to stand up for what I believe in and conviction to follow it through. If it were not for Stella, I would probably not have continued in long term care; not by choice, but I would have probably been fired eventually. I certainly should have been many times.

I have read studies on what residents appreciate most in a CNA. It is never skill – how well we bath them, feed them, or dress them – it is our attitudes when we enter their rooms. They count on our smiles, hugs, positive dispositions. If we live our professional lives in a near constant state of frustration and cannot first understand what is expected of us from those we serve, we cannot do the very thing we hold dear, and that is please our residents and make them happy. Once we understand this, it is then necessary to confront the issues that cause the frustration and either become part of the solution or let go of the things beyond our control and stay focused on our ability to meet the resident's needs.

Life Lesson # 9
**Each CNA has the ability to use
their influence to help patients
maintain their dignity or lose their dignity.
It is simply a matter of choice.**

Chapter Ten

What Next?

After being set straight and recommitting myself to the profession I love, I set out to make a greater difference in the world. If I could not change things in the facility as radically as I thought needed while being a CNA, I would have no choice but to get in a position of what I thought was real power. I would become a nursing home administrator. But wait – I'm a high school dropout who passed the GED by a whopping four points. I was enrolled in junior college which is supposed to only take two years, but I had already been going several.   How does one become an administrator anyway?

I had been a sassy, nursing assistant for much of my career. I kept a little memo pad in my lab coat pocket where I would write down the things I would do if I ever got to be in charge. My list included things like help make beds, help get residents up, pay the CNAs a higher wage, and help feed in the dining room and not just when state was there (ha ha) but all the time. I also had on the list my commitment not to hire any of the undesirable looking people like the many who had been hired by my administrator and nursing director throughout the years.

Each evening when I would get to work and get clocked in, I would go straight to the administrator or a supervisor and ask, "What is the census today?" They always had a strange look on their face like they were thinking what on earth does she need to know the census for? They did not always appreciate the question. I would then make a notation in my memo book and use it later to figure how much money the facility was making that day. It always seemed like a lot, and the CNAs weren't getting very much of it. I knew once in charge, I would change that immediately. I had not given any consideration to what things really cost and how much the facility was spending on food, medical supplies, salaries, and utilities. Boy, was I in for a rude awakening.

I kept my dream of becoming an administrator to myself for a long time. Then one day, I was summoned to the office by the administrator. Usually this meant trouble, but it had been months since my rededication to the profession, and I had not caused any problems so I was left wondering what this could be about. When I went in, the administrator said to me, "Lori, I have been watching you the past year, and you have really come a long way. I am very proud of your dedication and commitment to the residents. I know you are taking college classes, and I was just wondering what your long range plans are." She was being so complimentary saying things like you are a very smart, young woman who has a great deal of potential. I was now feeling pretty confident so I said to her, "Well, I really want to be a nursing home administrator just like you." Her facial expression changed considerably. She now looked almost sad as she said in a soft voice, "Oh, honey, you are just not administrator material. I have an activity assistant position open that I thought you might be interested in, but I could not in good faith encourage your administrator dream."

Oh, my goodness. I was so devastated. Me – not administrator material – I just couldn't believe it. But after all, she was an administrator and should know who has it and who doesn't. I said to her, "No thank you. If I can't be in charge, I prefer to continue being a CNA." I left her office feeling so low. I mean my whole dream collapsed in seconds. How could I not be administrator material, but obviously I was not. I just kept telling myself that I was not the right material based on her comments.

A few months had passed, and I was coming in for my evening shift from college when I noticed the administrator was carrying a box to her car. When I got inside, I asked the charge nurse what was going on, and she said, "The administrator's boss came in a few minutes earlier and fired her." What? She was fired? I thought to myself, "Well, I guess she must not be administrator material."

Dream back on! From that point on, I never let anyone else influence my belief in my dreams. Who was she to tell me I was not administrator material. I'll show her. And that I did. In 1989, a dream came true! I received my nursing home administrator's license in the state of Kansas. My first job was in a Kansas City, Kansas, suburb – a 54-bed facility, and I was on cloud nine.

Life Lesson # 10
Let no one influence your dreams and ambitions. Learn from them if they have something positive to teach you but remember, they can't read a crystal ball and predict your future nor are they <u>all</u> knowing.

Chapter Eleven

Realizing a Dream

I had made it. I was in charge. I had a new home for my memo pad as I had traded in my lab coat for a suit coat. It had not been an easy road to say the least. I failed the administrator's exam the first time I tested. Again, I was very disappointed. I remember on the way to Topeka I had allowed myself to think negative thoughts like how can I be an administrator, I was just a high school dropout. I'm not that smart. I know nothing about business management. If I fail, everyone back home will say things like, "That is what you get, trying to get above your raising."

I knew the material. I had studied hard and spent not only my last penny on the seminars and the textbooks, but my stepdad had loaned me the money to go to Topeka for the exam. It takes about three weeks to get the test results, so instead of going back home, I went to my brother's house to look for a job and await the results. When they arrived, I found I had not passed. What now? I just couldn't believe I had failed. I couldn't go back home. I did not want to go to work in a facility as a CNA, not because I was too good to be a CNA again, but I knew everyday when I went to work I would be reminded of my failure. Instead I took a job as an assistant manager of a cookie store in a Kansas City shopping mall. I was broke and very disappointed. It was Easter time and working in the cookie store I was required to wear bunny ears during the season and stand out in the corridor trying to get shoppers to sample the cookies. Boy, this will do a number on your self-esteem. I kept telling myself I was a failure – not smart enough, a high school dropout, and I was too fat and ugly to be successful.

As the weeks turned to months, I started paying close attention to those who bought cookies. Mostly we sold to mall employees. Many of these employees were managers of clothing stores or fashion buyers, mostly women. One day, while waiting on a customer who was dressed professionally and had a name tag on from a popular upscale clothing store, I realized that she was not great looking and was pretty overweight. I said to myself, "Damn, there are some fat, ugly successful women out there; I might as well be one of them!"

I immediately made an appointment to sit for the examination again, only this time I told myself on the drive there that I was ready. I knew the material the first time, so I did not even study the second time around. I just marched in there, took the exam, and drove back to Kansas City. I knew I had passed – I could just feel it. I drove the 70 miles back honking the horn every few minutes to celebrate my passing.

I got very lucky because a company that managed several homes hired me. They were willing to put me on as an administrator-in-training while we waited for the results of the examination. I was so lucky, I just couldn't believe it. Sure enough, the results came, and I had indeed passed with flying colors. You see, the only difference was my state of mind and what I was telling myself on the drives to Topeka. The first one was full of negative thoughts – self-doubt and negative self-talk; the second was full of positive thoughts – self-confidence and positive self-talk. I was finally a fully licensed administrator of a nursing home. Yippee! It was a great time.

Life Lesson # 11
The greatest test of courage on earth is to bear defeat without losing heart.
If at first you don't succeed, try try again.
It's as simple as that.

Chapter Twelve

When Dreams Turn to Nightmares

Almost immediately, my dream turned to a nightmare. I was very proud to be an administrator, but I was a small town girl trying to run a nursing home in a big city. The people were so different and seemed to be completely unmanageable. The home was severely understaffed because it was an older facility in a city where new fancy nursing homes had been built. Remember my memo pad with the list of things I would do when I got in charge? Well, I was making beds and feeding in the dining room – not just because I was trying to be the best administrator in the world but because I had to. There simply was not enough staff to meet the needs of the residents. Desperate situations lead to desperate measures.

Within the first few months, I had been through more than anyone should ever have to endure in their entire career. My boss at the time jokingly referred to it as my rookie season. I was performing any number of duties (depending on who called in or quit without notice) while playing receptionist, figuring up hours and doing payroll, trying to run the building, and meet and greet the community so we could get our census up. The facility was losing money, and I was losing my mind. The staff had a great deal of fun making my life miserable.

About a month into the position, and at the age of 26, I had to terminate a nursing director who was in her 50's. I was so nervous I questioned how I would ever get through it. One thing made it easier however. I had gotten a call the night before from the night shift laundry attendant telling me that the male and female CNAs on night shift were having sex in empty resident beds. WHAT? You have to be kidding? Not kidding! I went in to see for myself, and much to my surprise, it was indeed true. Now how does one handle this? Since I had been working so hard and was stressed out with absolutely no time for a personal life, I was already somewhat angry so I simply said, "If I'm not getting any, neither are you guys." I couldn't afford to fire anyone as I had no way of replacing them but they got the point! And it did make the job of terminating the nursing director a bit easier since she had allowed this behavior in the first place.

Christmas evening I came home from spending the day with friends and family to a frantic message on my machine left by the new director of nursing, "Get to the nursing home stat; there has been a gas leak!" This was a couple years before cell phones were in wide use, and we were too poor to afford one anyway (same reason I did not have a pager). Fortunately, the message had been left only minutes before I arrived home. By the time I got to the facility, they had several blocks roped off, and I had to park and run. It was unbelievable! We had to evacuate all residents for the night – coordinate transportation, secure a safe warm bed for each resident, make sure no one missed their medications – all with no means of communication. The power had been turned off to avoid creating any kind of sparks or electrical fires so the telephones were not functioning. A neighbor from across the street brought us her cordless phone which I used to make calls to place the residents. School buses came to transport them out of the cold to nearby places where they could be looked after. Not one single resident missed so much as a scheduled dose of Mylanta.

All this took place as a state inspector looked on criticizing our every move. She was not there to assist but monitor our work. What a deal! Here was a nurse who was hired by the state to protect the residents, and she spent the evening writing in her notebook. I knew then our system was badly flawed when you could not even count on them in a state of emergency.

In addition to the inspector, we had every major news network in the Kansas City area there covering the event – it was a major story! Thankfully, everything turned out OK. Our residents were able to return home the following afternoon, and soon we were back to the daily grind of trying to hire enough help and taking good care of our residents. The state, however, never left us alone following the gas leak incident even though there were no deficiencies cited. Everyone was singing our praises – the residents, their families, the community – everyone was telling us what an amazing job we did. Our new director of nursing was the most heroic. The gas leak was at the rear of the building just outside the boiler room where the hot water tank pilots were still in full flame. One of the first things she did was go directly into the most dangerous area and cut off the pilots. We might not have had enough staff, but those we did have were heroes that day.

With stress mounting, I found myself ready to quit. I had decided I am not the administrator I thought I could be and that nothing I tried was making a great enough difference. We needed

CNAs, and we needed them fast. I was completely out of ideas on how to recruit people to an old nursing home when the new spectacular facilities had more to offer.

I decided to treat myself to lunch outside the facility one day. While at lunch, I was very tempted to ask for bar seating where I could drown my sorrows or what felt more like failures. Instead, I did the right thing and stuck with a sandwich and iced tea. I can remember exactly what I ordered that day; as a matter of fact, I remember everything about that day. I truly contemplated quitting, just walking away. I knew, however, if I did, my career would be over. You can't abandon a nursing home without serious repercussions. I decided instead to spend the lunch hour going back to something that had worked in the past – positive self-talk. Now people often laugh when you talk about positive self-talk, but it does work. (There are times in your life when you do not have a big cheering squad behind you doing it for you.) I told myself things have to get better; just go back and walk in with enthusiasm and pride and the belief that things can and will turn around. You didn't become an administrator to fail.

It helped. I did go back, and the most amazing thing happened upon my return. I walked in, and through the nursing office window I could tell there was a young lady in there filling out an application. AH, HA! Positive self-talk does work

I told myself. OK, now all I have to do is muster up enough enthusiasm and motivation to go bouncing in there with words of wisdom which will make her want to accept a position on the team today! In I go through the door, and then I look down towards her. I had to do a double take because when I looked at her she was wearing hot pants, a halter top, and had three of the biggest, darkest hickies I had ever seen on the side of her neck. The memo book popped into my head, especially the line that said I will not hire any undesirables on my team. It popped out of my head as fast as it came in, and I leaned down to the young lady and said in desperation, "CAN YOU START TONIGHT?"

You see, no matter what your values start out to be they can easily be compromised when you do not have enough people to take care of the residents. I have unfortunately had to both work with and hire people I wished I hadn't had to. We all have. It is no one's fault; it is simply a symptom of our society. It isn't cool to grow old; therefore, many think it is not cool to seek positions caring for those who are old. I stuck it out as long as I could, and we eventually turned things around somewhat but not before a number of more almost catastrophic events. The little facility appeared to be doomed. It was quite a rookie season for me.

During my climb of achieving my dream to be an administrator, I became a study of what was required of one. Aside from making sure the residents were well cared for, it seemed an enormous amount of importance was put on making sure all the beds were full. After all, how else can a facility make money? It really doesn't matter if you work for a "for-profit" or "not-for-profit" facility – without residents, you have no income. I figured I could always land on top as an administrator if I could find a way to keep my beds filled.

I found the secret to marketing long term care facilities, but that will have to wait for my next book. What is important here is that is how my career progressed. I had mastered marketing, and although the facility finally was closed by the state, I emerged intact. I was a bit bumped and bruised, but I was OK and on my way to the corporate office to help manage six other facilities. My marketing skills had earned me the right to move up the ladder.

Life Lesson # 12
**Pay attention to what a person is now, not what he has been.
Don't let someone else's opinion of you destroy the opinion you have of yourself.
Don't take life to seriously – forgive and forget misunderstandings.
Love – real love is wanting nothing back in return.**

Chapter Thirteen

Yet Another Chapter and This One Deals With Karma

It was an extraordinary climb to the top of operations but a journey I am so blessed to have made. My life, and no doubt yours, is better because of long term care. It really is true – everything I learned, I learned in long term care. It was a great teacher of life's lessons.

It was now time to go back to a real dream I had one night in 1991. It was such a vivid dream, and the first time I remembered dreaming in color. I had formed a professional association of nursing assistants, and we were having a big convention.

CNAs had come from all across America to attend. I remembered standing around looking at the members and the decorations and realizing that this was the way to change long term care for the better. This was an opportunity for all of us who have said many times CNAs are the backbone to the facility. I knew that most any problem that had occurred in the nursing homes I had worked in as a CNA and those I had been managing could be solved by the CNAs if given a chance. We didn't have to be short-handed; we did not have to have deficiencies; and most importantly, we could find ways to ensure our residents had the best care and the best quality of life. There did not have to be excessive call-ins, and there really wasn't any reason CNAs could not solve the problem of negativity in the workplace. In lay the solution to most all challenges with the CNAs even if they did not recognize their problem-solving abilities.

When I woke from this dream, I remember feeling really excited but afraid to tell anyone for fear they would laugh or make fun of the idea. If it were such a great idea, how come no one else had thought of it? However, I was just about to bust. Later that afternoon, I went riding with a friend and her mother in her mom's convertible. The day was so sweet, the air amazing, and the wind blowing through our hair. I got so caught up in it, I blurted out my dream – out loud in front of real people! They didn't laugh; they actually said, "What a great

idea; you should pursue it. Make it happen!"
What? I am only one person. I am a high school dropout; how can I set up a professional association and get anyone to pay attention?

Well, in 1991 I took their advice. I started the National Association of Geriatric Nursing Assistants (NAGNA). I wish I could tell you it was a booming success, but I can't. You see, it failed – or I should say I quit trying before it had a chance to take off.

I had spent so much of my life up to that point struggling financially. The previous three years marked the first time I could pay my bills on time, go to the doctor when I was sick, and start rebuilding my credit in hopes of buying a home one day. So when I started having financial difficulties again, I panicked. Within a few months, I had exhausted what little savings I had, so I quickly put my dream on the backburner. But I have to tell you that I felt defeated because I was giving up on my dream.   Thank goodness it wouldn't be long before NAGNA would be revived and for good this time. What you sometimes can't do alone you can do with some else's knowledge and support.

I continued to publish a small newsletter (about 50 copies every other month) and sent them to the few CNAs who had joined during that first few months while I began looking for my next administrator's job. It wasn't long before I found one; however, I had to move back to the area in which I had grown up.

There is no end to the experiences I have had in long term care. We have all had incredible experiences which shaped our lives and taught us valuable lessons. When I was 15, I was snowed in at my best friend's house. She lived on a small farm, and her parents were fairly well to do. Her dad was in politics; her mother was involved in the community. Well, there was little to do at their house in a snowstorm except for hanging out in the barn talking and smoking cigarettes, and that is exactly what we did. The snow eventually broke, and Mom came and picked me up. My friend put the cigs in one of her clothing drawers, and later that night, her mother was putting away the laundry and discovered the cigarettes. "WHOSE ARE THESE?" she demanded. My friend, trying to escape the wrath, said, "They are Lori's." From that moment on I was no good, a bad influence, and she was instructed never to hang around or associate with me again. My friend complied for the most part. What a tragedy. We were good buddies, and we loved the game of basketball. Soon other parents found out about the smoking and forbade their kids from hanging out with me. Not long after, I quit school. I thought my life was over – all these people thought I was no good, a bad influence, trash. I left that area vowing never to return.

Now I found myself returning as the new administrator of 120-bed facility just a few miles from my hometown. I was reluctant but Mom had moved back and was living near there, and she was getting older. I knew it would be nice to be near her plus I was an adult, and after all, I was a business woman now responsible for other people's lives. Well, I had no more accepted the job until someone asked me, "Did you know so and so's (my cigarette smoking friend) mother became a nurse and works at the facility where you are going? WHAT? OH MY GOD! You are kidding? Not kidding! What do I do now? I have to get out of this somehow. The woman ruined my life once (so I thought), and I can't let her do it again. It's incredible the power we give some people over our lives. I called my new boss and said, "I have made a terrible mistake. I have to back out." "Not so fast," she replied. "I am counting on you. You are supposed to start in a week." Well, I had no choice but to go forward. Incredible dynamics were already going on because the director of nursing there had been my DON when I was a CNA. She had been good to me, and I was looking forward to working with her again.

I have to admit I got some delight out of being the boss this time; however, this new twist with my friend's mother had me paralyzed. I wondered, could she ruin my reputation? Could she make these people think I'm trash? Could she undermine my authority? Could she keep people from following my leadership and respecting me as a leader? By the time my first day arrived, I was so nervous I was sick.

My new boss spent the first day or so with me, introducing me around and making sure I was settled. It wasn't long on that first day before we were approaching my friend's mother. I could see her down at the end of the hall with the med cart. We continued walking her way – my knees were shaking, my stomach was churning, my hands were sweaty, and I just knew I was going to vomit. When we approached, my boss asked her, "Do you know Lori Porter?" I froze awaiting her response. Would she say, "Yes, I know the little troublemaker." No. She said, "Why yes, she practically grew up in my house!" That was certainly not the way I remembered it. Either I had totally misjudged the smoking incident and the years that followed or she lacked the courage to back up her actions and the way she felt about me when I was a 15-year-old kid – all for smoking cigarettes. Either way, things were going to be just fine. Each day she reported to work, it was basically an admission that I was not trash!

Months later I learned she was as afraid as I was because she just knew I would fire her. Later in that day, the director of nursing said to me, "I sure am glad I was good to you when you worked for me because paybacks can be hell." I noticed my friend's mother was standing near, and I said, "Yes, they can, and you just never know who is going to grow up and be your boss someday." Nothing more was ever said about the smoking incident and life went on. My friend's mother and I are actually close now. She is a great nurse. She's a bit strict as a supervisor, just as she was a mother, but her children turned out well – we all turned out well. Amen.

Life Lesson # 13
**Every time one person expresses an idea,
he finds ten people who thought of it before - -
but they only thought.**

Chapter Fourteen

One Last Tale
(dedicated to Ms. Stella Parrish)

During my CNA years, I had peaks and valleys in terms of my attitude. There were times I was great and others when I was a no-good, griping employee spreading negativity to all I could find. After falling into the long term care negative trap, I left for greener pastures only to realize there weren't any so back I went within a year or so.

Both times, I worked at this facility with a woman named Stella Parrish. Stella was an older lady. We young CNAs did not associate with her much or she with us, but she was always there and always the consummate professional. One night in the breakroom, I was causing a stink moaning and groaning about not having enough help. When are they going to hire us some more help? When are they going to pay us more? I was going on and on, and some people were agreeing with me, others were minding their own business – all except Stella. She was sitting at the long breakroom table down from me eating her lunch when she looked up and asked, "How long have you worked here now?" I said in a dull and sassy voice, "Six months, and it has been the longest six months of my life!" She said, "Well, I have been here years, and it has been the longest six months of my life too!" WOW! What a zinger that was. I thought who does this old bat think she is talking to me this way. She went on to say, "This place means something to me. I work hard, and I will not sit here and listen to you tear the place down like this. You know, you are a pretty good aide, at least you were when you were here before. Your attitude, however, is going to kill you. We need good nursing assistants, but we don't need anyone that badly." She continued, "Did you ever think this might not be your line of work?" I was in shock, but that last statement hit me like a tone of bricks because Ms. Punton had asked me that very question while I was disrespecting her.

I realized then that yes, this is my line of work – I love it, I am good at it. I thought about reporting Stella but who would take my side over a woman who had never missed a day of service? A woman so committed? I was embarrassed and ashamed, but I did know I had only two choices – get better or get out. I got better.

Years later when I came back to the facility where my friend's mother and my old DON worked, who else was working there but Stella Parrish. She had taken the job a few years before so she could shorten her drive to work. She was starting to get up in years but was just as dedicated and could work circles around gals half her age. In a small town, everyone knows everyone, and people just knew I would fire Stella to seek revenge for her embarrassing me that night in the breakroom. I have to admit I thought about it. (I mean, what good is being in charge if you can't take advantage of the perks.) But I would never fire Stella because I never forgot what she did for me. That night in the breakroom, she changed my course of action and my direction, and thanks to Stella, I was now enjoying a career I loved and about to revisit that important dream I had dreamt in 1991.

Lisa Cantrell and I worked at the facility together. She was a sharp, registered nurse who, like me, had gotten her start as a CNA. We had similar stories, and we certainly shared an appreciation for CNAs. I shared with her my dream, and she said, 'Let's do it. Let's make it happen." I said, "Oh, that won't work, I tried. People will now think it's bogus." She said, "Let's try anyway." This time we basically took a vow of poverty. Whatever it took, we would not get scared and run. We will stay the course. It was "if we build, they will come" kind of commitment. Well, we did go broke, but we have more than 30,000 members to prove that NAGNA was needed and is succeeding, and most importantly, all those challenges and problems that are crippling long term care can indeed be solved by CNAs.

The eight years that NAGNA has been in existence has proven that if you can stick it out and believe in your dreams, they really do come true. There have been so many highs to justify any sacrifices that were made. NAGNA is my pride and joy, and it provides all the validation one needs to see that not only are CNAs the backbone to long term care but its heart and soul!

The End

Life Lesson # 14
**When you get to the end of your rope,
tie a knot and hang on.
Long term care has taught me
that dreams really do come true
if you hang on long enough.
I've learned it is better to be a "nobody"
who accomplishes something than a
"somebody" who accomplishes nothing.**

In Loving Memory of a Great Woman

Stella Irene Parrish, CNA, CMT
1920 – 2003

NAGNA's Lifetime Achievement Award bears the name of Stella Parrish for her example of lifetime achievement in the CNA profession and her influence on my own career and development.

The Stella Parrish Lifetime Achievement Award was presented to the first recipient in 1995, the year of NAGNA's first annual awards banquet where Stella served as co-presenter of the award. Since that time, NAGNA has honored eight CNAs from across the nation for their resemblance to Stella's determination, commitment, and loyalty to her profession and to the residents in their charge.

Stella worked over 30 years as a CNA. According to personnel records, she did not miss a single day of service during her career until the day in 1998 when she was involved in a near fatal car accident and became a resident in the same facility where she had spent years caring for others.

I attended her funeral service on February 22, 2003, where I said goodbye to the best CNA I ever worked with and the best employee I ever had, not to mention a woman I, like many, was proud to call friend.

If you have ever asked yourself one or more of these questions, Lori Porter's presentations are for you!

How will we ever get the right kind of help?
How can I reduce turnover?
How can we recruit the best people in our community?
How do I motivate the staff I have?
Why is the staff running off the people we do hire?

Inquire about a live presentation/keynote speaking engagement by Lori Porter. Lori's presentations are guaranteed to revitalize health care audiences by getting her message across in her own uniquely animated and humorous style. As co-founder and CEO of NAGNA, Lori and her team have spent over 75,000 hours with the front-line staff and their management teams. Her unique experience makes her presentation one which takes you on a roller coaster of emotions and will no doubt rank among the best you will ever attend.

Target audiences: Long Term Care Providers Groups, State and National Health Care Associations, Anyone from frontline to the corporate staff.

Listen to What People Are Saying…..

"If you want practical, reality-based solutions to recruiting, retaining, and recognizing your front-line, don't miss her dynamic presentations. Lori is one of the best educators in long term care." – Mary Tellis-Nayak, President/CEO, American College of Health Care Administrators

"Lori's message is one that every person in our profession needs to hear and will be changed by. She provides education, motivation, and information that can address issues facilities are facing from a practical standpoint. You cannot escape unchanged, and you will have the tools that you need to begin making positive changes immediately." – Lorraine Tarnove, Executive Director, American Medical Directors Association

"I have seen Lori speak – to 1,000 people. She is fantastic! As one whose entire career has been based on professional speaking, I am stunned by Lori's timing, humor, connection with her audience, and message. She truly lifts people up who need a lift! This is the only thing she should be doing!" – John G. Miller, author of QBQ! The Question Behind the Question.

Inquiries on scheduling: 800-784-6049 or by e-mail: info@nagna.org.

To obtain additional or volume copies of *Everything I Learned in Life...I Learned in Long Term Care* go to our Web site at www.nagna.org (NAGNA Mall). Lori Porter's insight and experiences on her road to the top will both entertain and inform aspiring administrators and those wishing to learn more about long term care. Volume discounts are available.

To inquire about obtaining copies of Lori Porter's first book, *Take it to Heart: CNAs Solutions to the Staffing Crisis,* go to our Web site at www.nagna.org (NAGNA Mall). Lori maintains that until decision makers are reached at the heart level, change will not occur. The message sent comes from listening and watching thousands of dedicated CNAs, and readers will discover how to end the staffing crisis in long term care.

The audio presentation, *Your Daily Dose of Successful Thinking,* is available online at www.nagna.org (NAGNA Mall). This audio is a "must have" to harness the power of positive attitude. Lori Porter and Lisa Cantrell share their experiences on the awesome topics of motivation and positive attitude.

"*CNA Today,* NAGNA's quarterly publication for professional Nursing Assistants, was a dream in 1995," says Lori Porter, Managing Editor. Premiered at NAGNA's 2001 annual National Convention in Joplin, Missouri, *CNA Today* has become a powerful vehicle for CNAs to have a national voice and presence. It delivers a strong, positive message about the CNA profession. As the first national publication of its kind dedicated to Certified Nursing Assistants, *CNA Today* helps educate, advocate, and inspire CNAs across the country and informs others about the rigors of working within long term care.

Available through subscription and online at www.cnatoday.com.

Call 800-784-6049 for information on volume discounts.

Gift subscriptions available – a wonderful way to recognize dedicated staff members.

Affordable annual rates for NAGNA members ($10) and non-members ($15).

Reader base well over 20,000 – advertising opportunities available.

Articles/manuscripts always welcomed.

For inquiries on subscriptions, advertising, and articles, contact the editor of *CNA Today* at 800-784-6049 or by e-mail: info@cnatoday.com.

CNA "Hall of Fame"

The CNA "Hall of Fame," housed at the headquarters of the National Association of Geriatric Nursing Assistants in Joplin, Missouri, is a formal tribute to those Certified Nursing Assistants who have dedicated their lives to caregiving. Inductees into this prestigious "Hall of Fame" qualify by completing at least 20 years of service as a CNA. Employers nominate their Certified Nursing Assistants based on outstanding care rendered and professional dedication to caregiving. Bronzed, portrait plaques hang as a tribute to the dedicated CNAs who qualify and are formally inducted into this "Hall of Caregiving Fame."

The "CNA Hall of Fame" is available for viewing online at www.nagna.org and in person at the NAGNA Headquarters located at 2709 W. 13th Street, Joplin, Missouri, from 8 a.m. to 5 p.m., Monday through Friday.

Members speak out…

"Before NAGNA, I was just a staff member. I was someone who came to work, punched in, did a good job taking care of my residents but never realized how important I really am. Now I feel I am a part of a team – a giant team of professional CNAs. Through NAGNA, I have been given so many amazing opportunities to make an even greater difference!" Beth McCarty, CNA

For inquiries about membership and consulting services, call 800-784-6049 or go online at: www.nagna.org.

United in Caring

Listed below are reasons to become a member in the National Association of Geriatric Nursing Assistants:

> NAGNA's mission is to elevate the professional standing and performance of Certified Nursing Assistants through recognition, advocacy, education, and empowerment while building a stronger alliance with health care providers to maximize success and quality patient care.
>
> Nursing Assistants who participate in NAGNA are more connected to their profession and to their facilities.
>
> Informed and educated Nursing Assistants included in the operations of their facility strive for the highest quality of care for their residents.
>
> When recognized as professionals, CNAs take personal ownership and accountability for the success of their facilities.

NAGNA's educational programs and professional development courses are combined in the first ever CNA Institute for Professsional Development. The Institute endeavors to provide educational and personal growth that enables the student to reach their maximum potential and have a greater understanding of the complex long term care profession, the elderly, and the aging process.

Membership includes:

A national platform for CNAs to tell their stories.

Networking and fellowship.

Leadership opportunities.

Personal and family assistance.

Affordable health care benefits.

Group purchasing discounts.